rockschool®

POPULAR MUSIC THEORY

Workbook

GRADE 3

Acknowledgements

Published by Rockschool Ltd. © 2015
Catalogue Number RSK011506
ISBN: 978-1-908920-72-0

Publishing
Written, compiled and edited by Simon Troup, Jennie Troup and Stuart Slater.
Internal design and layout by Simon and Jennie Troup, Digital Music Art.
Cover designed by Philip Millard, Philip Millard Design.
Additional proofing by Chris Bird, Owen Bailey, Nik Preston, Mike Stylianou, Joanna Taman and Mary Keene.

Syllabus Consultants
Rachael Meech, Mike Stylianou, Joanna Taman and Anna Cook.

Contributors
Prof. Joe Bennett, Simon Niblock, Jonathan Preiss, Stefan Redtenbacher, Philip Henderson and Martin Hibbert.

Images & Illustrations
p. 24 | © LittleMiss / Shutterstock.com
p. 25 | ⓒⓒ interestedbystandr (tinyurl.com/pjen5tj)
p. 26 | © iStock.com/dlewis33
p. 26 | © iStock.com/cimmerian
p. 26 | © iStock.com/konkrete
p. 26 | © iStock.com/ladiras
pp. 27 & 51 | © grmarc / Shutterstock.com
pp. 27 & 51 | © mitay20 / Shutterstock.com
p. 50 | © Richard Schramm / Shutterstock.com
p. 50 | © Dean Bertoncelj / Shutterstock.com

Printing
Printed and bound in the United Kingdom by Caligraving Ltd.

Distribution
Exclusive Distributors: Music Sales Ltd.

Contacting Rockschool
www.rockschool.co.uk
Telephone: +44 (0)845 460 4747
Email: info@rockschool.co.uk

Table of Contents

Introductions & Information

Page

Theory Exam Sections

Page

Sample Paper

Page

Additional Information

Page

Welcome to Rockschool Popular Music Theory – Grade 3

Rockschool publish two sets of books to help candidates prepare for theory examinations – the *Rockschool Popular Music Theory Guidebooks* and *Rockschool Popular Music Theory Workbooks.*

The guidebooks are a teaching resource for candidates to work through the material required for the Rockschool theory syllabus with the support of their teacher.

To complement the guidebooks, a set of workbooks provide a series of exercises and sample papers in which to practise the skills introduced in the guidebooks.

Entering Rockschool Examinations
It's now easier than ever to enter a Rockschool examination. Simply go to *www.rockschool.co.uk/enter-online* to book your exam online today.

Syllabus Content Overview
An overview of the syllabus content covered at this grade can be found at the back of this book. As this is a cumulative syllabus, you can download overviews for all grades from the Rockschool website at *www.rockschool.co.uk/theory* along with other theory syllabus related resources.

Exam Format
The exam has four sections. These are:

- **Music Notation** (20%)
  In this section, all questions relate to music notation.

- **Popular Music Harmony** (25%)
  In this section, all questions relate to music harmony.

- **Band Knowledge** (25%)
  This section is in two parts, with each part covering a range of instruments:
    – **Part 1:** Identification
    – **Part 2:** Notation and Techniques

- **Band Analysis** (30%)
  In this section, the questions will include the identification of music notation, harmony and the stylistic characteristics of drums, guitar, bass, keys and vocals in a multi-instrumental context.

Section 1 | Music Notation

SUMMARY	
SECTION *(Current section highlighted)*	**MARKS**
> **Music Notation**	**20 [20%]**
Popular Music Harmony	25 [25%]
Band Knowledge	25 [25%]
Band Analysis	30 [30%]

The *Music Notation* section of Rockschool Theory Examinations covers the following:

- 1.1   Pitch
- 1.2   Note length/rhythm
- 1.3   Dynamics, articulations and phrasing

You will be presented with a variety of exercises to hone your understanding and skills in these areas within the content specified for this grade.

Content Overview

An overview of the syllabus content covered at this grade can be found at the back of this book. As this is a cumulative syllabus, you can download overviews for all grades from the Rockschool website at *www.rockschool.co.uk*.

Section 1 | Music Notation

Note lengths | Adding barlines

1. Add barlines to the following stave, ensuring that there are the correct number of beats in each bar:

2. Add barlines to the following stave, ensuring that there are the correct number of beats in each bar:

3. Add barlines to the following stave, ensuring that there are the correct number of beats in each bar:

Note lengths | Add the time signature

1. Add the correct time signature to the start of the following stave:

2. Add the correct time signature to the start of the following stave:

3. Add the correct time signature to the start of the following stave:

Note lengths | Add the missing notes

1. Add a note of the correct length above each question mark so that each bar matches the time signature:

2. Add a note of the correct length above each question mark so that each bar matches the time signature:

3. Add a note of the correct length above each question mark so that each bar matches the time signature:

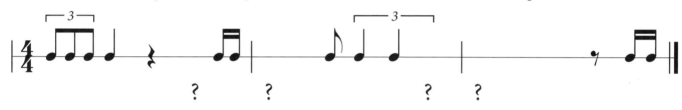

Note lengths | Beaming notes correctly

1. Rewrite the music in bars 1 & 2 into bars 3 & 4, connecting the notes with beams where appropriate:

2. Rewrite the music in bars 1 & 2 into bars 3 & 4, connecting the notes with beams where appropriate:

3. Rewrite the music in bars 1 & 2 into bars 3 & 4, connecting the notes with beams where appropriate:

Section 1 | Music Notation

Note names | Add the correct clef

1. Add the correct clef to the beginning of the stave below to make a scale. Finally, tick the correct scale name in the box below the stave:

☐ E♭ major   ☐ C natural minor   ☐ B♭ major

2. Add the correct clef to the beginning of the stave below to make a scale. Finally, tick the correct scale name in the box below the stave:

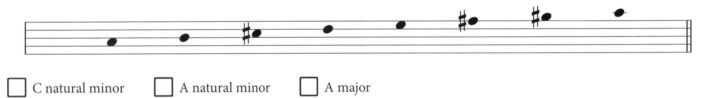

☐ G major   ☐ B natural minor   ☐ D major

3. Add the correct clef to the beginning of the stave below to make a scale. Finally, tick the correct scale name in the box below the stave:

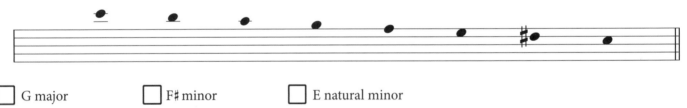

☐ C natural minor   ☐ A natural minor   ☐ A major

4. Add the correct clef to the beginning of the stave below to make a scale. Finally, tick the correct scale name in the box below the stave:

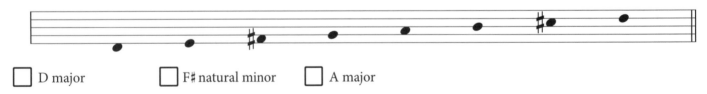

☐ G major   ☐ F♯ minor   ☐ E natural minor

5. Add the correct clef to the beginning of the stave below to make a scale. Finally, tick the correct scale name in the box below the stave:

☐ D major   ☐ F♯ natural minor   ☐ A major

6. Add the correct clef to the beginning of the stave below to make a scale. Finally, tick the correct scale name in the box below the stave:

☐ F♯ natural minor   ☐ F♯ major   ☐ A major

Rests | Add the missing rests

1. Add a rest of the correct length to the music where indicated by each of the **three** question marks:

2. Add a rest of the correct length to the music where indicated by each of the **three** question marks:

3. Add a rest of the correct length to the music where indicated by each of the **three** question marks:

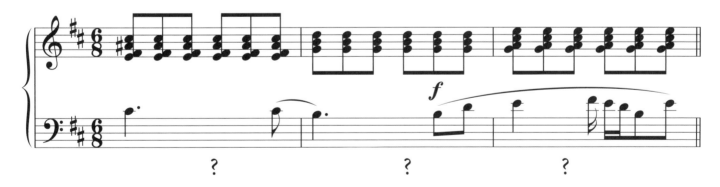

Section 1 | Music Notation

Repeats | Segno, Coda and Fine

1. Write down the sequence of letters that represents the order in which the following bars are played from start to finish:

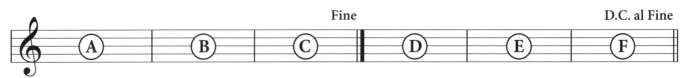

Your answer:

2. Write down the sequence of letters that represents the order in which the following bars are played from start to finish:

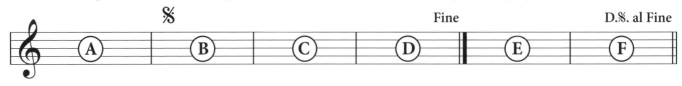

Your answer:

3. Write down the sequence of letters that represents the order in which the following bars are played from start to finish:

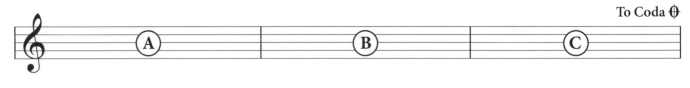

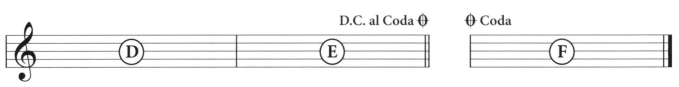

Your answer:

4. Write down the sequence of letters that represents the order in which the following bars are played from start to finish:

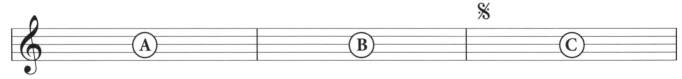

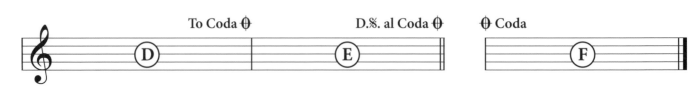

Your answer:

Dynamics & Articulations | Identifying dynamics

1. Answer the questions below relating to the following passage of music:

Which bar or bars contain a crescendo?

....

Which bar or bars are played at the same volume throughout?

....

Which bar or bars contain a diminuendo?

....

Which bar has the quietest note?

....

Which bar contains the musical symbol pianissimo?

....

Which bar contains an accent?

....

Which articulation is used on every note in bar 4?

....

Section 1 | Music Notation

Dynamics & Articulations | Identifying dynamics

1. Write one of the following musical symbols in each box, ensuring that they are arranged from quietest to loudest as directed by the arrow. Finally, write the name of the symbol on the line below each box:

$$mp \quad f \quad p \quad pp \quad ff \quad mf$$

Quietest ⟶ Loudest

_____   _____   _____   _____   _____   _____

Dynamics & Articulations | Identifying articulations

1. Complete the blank spaces in the table below with information relating to the articulations in the column on the left:

SYMBOL	MUSICAL TERM	MEANING
~~ (notehead)		
3 (triplet)		Three eighth notes played in the space of two eighth-notes
D.C.		
D.S.		
(fermata symbol)	Fermata	
♪♪ = triplet figure		

Section 2 | Popular Music Harmony

SUMMARY

The *Popular Music Harmony* section of Rockschool Theory Examinations covers the following:

- 2.1 Scales and related intervals
- 2.2 Simple triadic chords

You will be presented with a variety of exercises to hone your understanding and skills in these areas within the content specified for this grade.

Content Overview

An overview of the syllabus content covered at this grade can be found at the back of this book. As this is a cumulative syllabus, you can download overviews for all grades from the Rockschool website at *www.rockschool.co.uk*.

Section 2 | Popular Music Harmony

Intervals | Identifying intervals

1. Identify the following melodic intervals by ticking the correct box below each example:

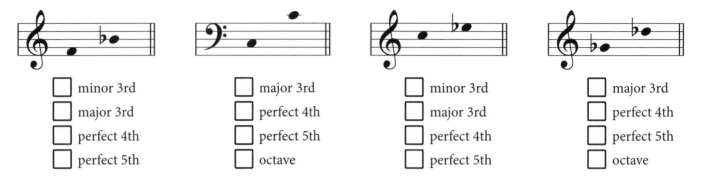

☐ minor 3rd
☐ major 3rd
☐ perfect 4th
☐ perfect 5th

☐ major 3rd
☐ perfect 4th
☐ perfect 5th
☐ octave

☐ minor 3rd
☐ major 3rd
☐ perfect 4th
☐ perfect 5th

☐ major 3rd
☐ perfect 4th
☐ perfect 5th
☐ octave

2. Add a note of the requested harmonic interval **above** each of the following notes:

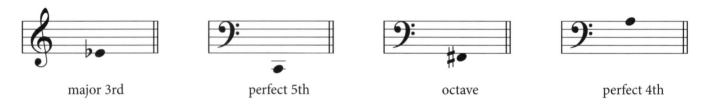

major 3rd   perfect 5th   octave   perfect 4th

3. Add a note of the requested harmonic interval **above** each of the following notes:

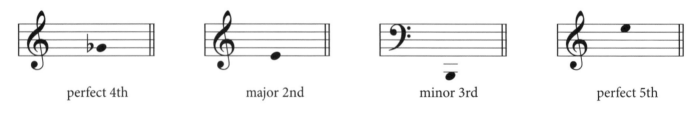

perfect 4th   major 2nd   minor 3rd   perfect 5th

Intervals | Applying interval knowledge

1. Draw a circle around consecutive notes which are either a perfect 4th or a perfect 5th apart (one instance of each):

2. Draw a circle around consecutive notes which are either a perfect 4th or a perfect 5th apart (one instance of each):

Scales | Identifying scale intervals

1. Add the appropriate key signature for the A major scale, then write 'T' in boxes between notes that are a **T**one apart, and write 'S' in boxes between notes that are a **S**emitone apart:

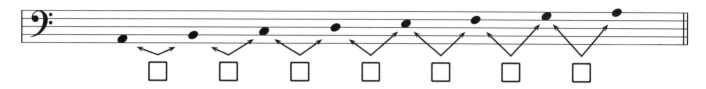

2. Add the appropriate key signature for the C natural minor scale, then write 'T' in boxes between notes that are a **T**one apart, and write 'S' in boxes between notes that are a **S**emitone apart:

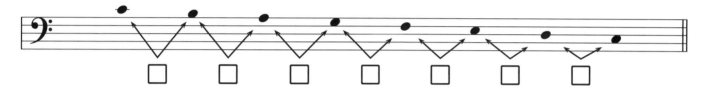

3. Add the appropriate key signature for the D major scale, then write 'T' in boxes between notes that are a **T**one apart, and write 'S' in boxes between notes that are a **S**emitone apart:

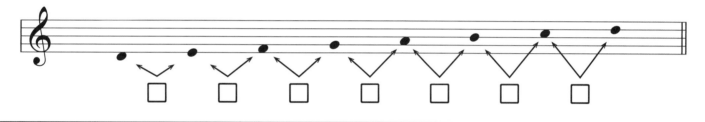

Scales | Writing scales with accidentals

1. Using whole notes, write a one-octave *descending* scale of E♭ major. Do *not* use a key signature; instead, add accidentals where necessary:

2. Using whole notes, write a one-octave *ascending* scale of F♯ natural minor. Do *not* use a key signature; instead, add accidentals where necessary:

3. Using whole notes, write a one-octave *descending* scale of B♭ major. Do *not* use a key signature; instead, add accidentals where necessary:

Section 2 | Popular Music Harmony

Scales | Major pentatonic and minor pentatonic scales

The following three questions require an understanding of relative major and relative minor scales. We use the term 'relative counterpart' to refer to the relative major or relative minor of the scale in question (e.g. the 'relative counterpart' of the G major pentatonic scale is the E minor pentatonic scale).

1. Name the following scale and then write out and name its relative counterpart on the empty stave below:

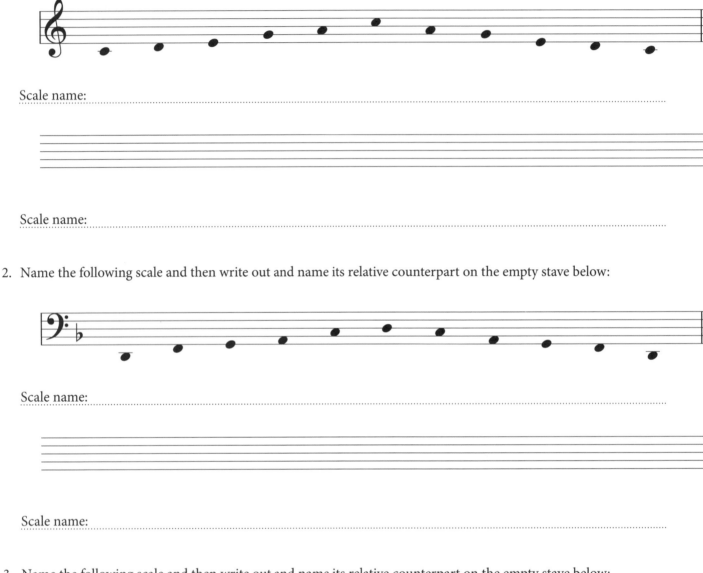

Scale name: ....

Scale name: ....

2. Name the following scale and then write out and name its relative counterpart on the empty stave below:

Scale name: ....

Scale name: ....

3. Name the following scale and then write out and name its relative counterpart on the empty stave below:

Scale name: ....

Scale name: ....

Scales | Pentatonic melodies

1. Circle the note that isn't from the G major pentatonic scale:

Name the note that isn't in the G major pentatonic scale: ....

What is the relative minor pentatonic scale of G major pentatonic? ....

Which notes from the G major scale are not in G major pentatonic? ....

2. Circle the two notes that aren't from the C minor pentatonic scale:

Name the two notes that aren't from the C minor pentatonic scale: ....

What is the relative major pentatonic scale of C minor pentatonic? ....

Which notes from C natural minor do not appear in C minor pentatonic? ....

Section 2 | Popular Music Harmony

Scales | Applying scale knowledge

1. Are there any wrong notes in this E♭ major scale? *(Tick one box)*

   E♭   F   G   A   B♭   C   D   E♭

   ☐ Yes   ☐ No

2. Put circles around any notes that are **not** in the F♯ natural minor scale:

   D♯   E♭   F   G♯   A♮   B♭   C♯   D♮   E   F♯   G♮   A

3. Write out the letter names (with their accidentals if appropriate) of the B natural minor scale:

   Your answer: ....

4. One or more accidentals are missing from this A major scale, underline any wrong notes and add their accidentals:

   A   B   C   D   E   F♯   G   A

5. Are there any wrong notes in this C natural minor scale? *(Tick one box)*

   C   D   E♭   F   G   A♭   B♭   C

   ☐ Yes   ☐ No

6. Look at each note in turn, circling those that can be found in the B♭ major scale:

   B♭   G♮   E   D   C♯   F   A   D♭   A♮   G   E♮   F♯   B   C

7. Briefly describe the function of a 'flat' sign:

   Your answer: ....

Arpeggios | Identifying arpeggios

1. This is an A major arpeggio. Add the correct clef and key signature:

2. This is an E minor arpeggio. Add the correct clef and key signature:

3. This is an E♭ major arpeggio. Add the correct clef and key signature:

4. Using whole notes, complete the stave below by adding the notes of a one-octave *ascending* and *descending* arpeggio in the **minor** key shown by the clef and key signature:

5. Using whole notes, complete the stave below by adding the notes of a one-octave *ascending* and *descending* arpeggio in the **minor** key shown by the clef and key signature:

6. Using whole notes, complete the stave below by adding the notes of a one-octave *ascending* and *descending* arpeggio in the **major** key shown by the clef and key signature:

Section 2 | Popular Music Harmony

Chords | Harmonised major scales

1. Identify the following chords from a harmonised C major scale using Roman numerals:

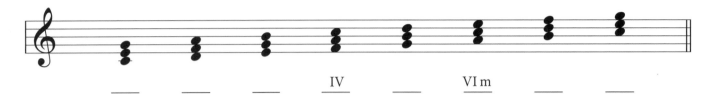

_____ _____ _____ IV _____ VI m _____ _____

2. Identify the following chords using Roman numerals:

F major

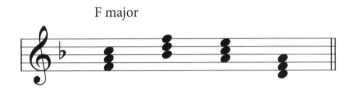

_____ _____ _____ _____

A major

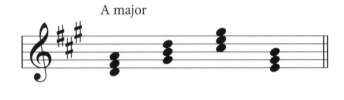

_____ _____ _____ _____

3. Identify the following chords using Roman numerals:

B♭ major

_____ _____ _____ _____

D major

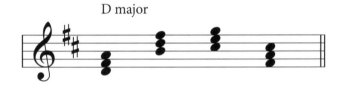

_____ _____ _____ _____

Chords | Chords charts

1. Identify the chords from the following chord chart using Roman numerals:

I _____ _____ _____ _____ _____ _____ _____

2. Identify the chords from the following chord chart using Roman numerals:

I _____ _____ _____ _____ _____ _____ _____

3. Identify the chords from the following chord chart using Roman numerals:

I _____ _____ _____ _____ _____ _____ _____

Chords | Writing chords

1. Add the notes of the triads given in Roman numerals for the following major keys:

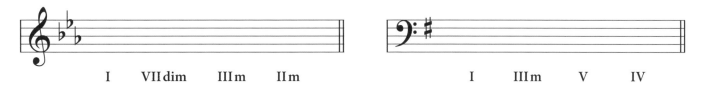

I   VIIdim   IIIm   IIm   I   IIIm   V   IV

2. Add the notes of the triads given in Roman numerals for the following major keys:

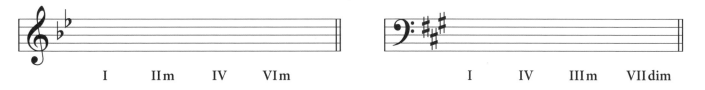

I   IIm   IV   VIm   I   IV   IIIm   VIIdim

3. Add the notes of the triads given in Roman numerals for the following major keys:

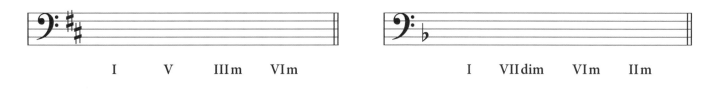

I   V   IIIm   VIm   I   VIIdim   VIm   IIm

Chords | Creating chord charts from Roman numerals

1. Add the chord symbols suggested by the Roman numerals below the stave for the key indicated in the first bar:

G major

2. Add the chord symbols suggested by the Roman numerals below the stave for the key indicated in the first bar:

B♭ major

3. Add the chord symbols suggested by the Roman numerals below the stave for the key indicated in the first bar:

E♭ major

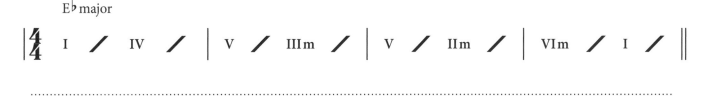

Section 2 | Popular Music Harmony

Chords | Applying chord knowledge

1. Using your knowledge of chords and the principle of relative major and relative minor keys, draw lines connecting each chord on the left with its counterpart on the right. For example, an A minor chord should be connected to a C major chord because their keys are related. Finally, add the name of each chord on the line below each stave:

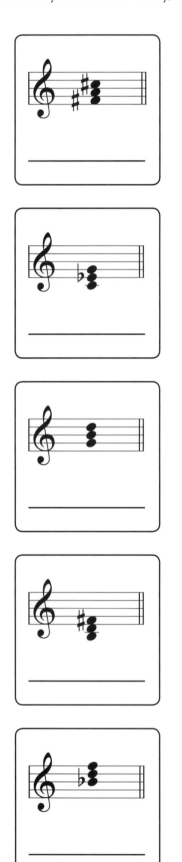

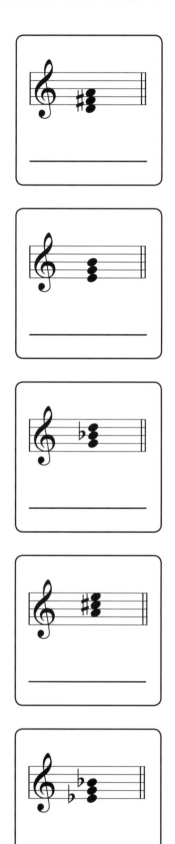

SECTION 3 | BAND KNOWLEDGE

SUMMARY	
SECTION *(Current section highlighted)*	**MARKS**
Music Notation	20 [20%]
Popular Music Harmony	25 [25%]
> **Band Knowledge**	**25 [25%]**
Band Analysis	30 [30%]

The *Band Knowledge* section of Rockschool Theory Examinations covers the following:

- 3.1 Identify instrument parts and function
- 3.2 Identify instrument-specific notation
- 3.3 Identify instrumental techniques

You will be presented with a variety of exercises to hone your understanding and skills in these areas within the content specified for this grade.

Content Overview

An overview of the syllabus content covered at this grade can be found at the back of this book. As this is a cumulative syllabus, you can download overviews for all grades from the Rockschool website at *www.rockschool.co.uk*.

Section 3 | Band Knowledge

Part 1 | Identification | Drums

1. What is the item in the image on the right used for? *(Tick one box)*

   ☐ To lock a drum to the stand.

   ☐ To tune the drums.

   ☐ To change the angle of a cymbal.

   ☐ To raise the height of a hi-hat.

True or false:

2. Cymbal stands are usually floor standing: ☐ True ☐ False

3. Cymbals are usually mounted on the bass drum: ☐ True ☐ False

4. A boom stand is a common type of cymbal stand: ☐ True ☐ False

5. A cymbal stand is usually mounted on wheels: ☐ True ☐ False

6. Most cymbal stands have a tripod base: ☐ True ☐ False

---

7. Connect each of the boxes on the left with a box on the right by drawing a line between to connect them, matching the text on the left with the closest match on the right:

Bass drum	Usually mounted above the bass drum in pairs
Hi-hat	A drum with a metal rattle beneath the base
Crash	The largest instrument in the drum kit
Snare drum	Consists of two cymbals, a stand and a foot pedal
Toms	A common cymbal used for occasional accents

Part 1 | Identification | Guitar and Bass

1. Which of the following is a type of tuning peg? *(Tick one box)*

   ☐ Machine head

   ☐ Tuning fork

   ☐ Strap button

   ☐ Turnpike

   ☐ Pin head

---

2. Which of the following properties is essential to the way guitar pickups work? *(Tick one box)*

   ☐ Magnetic

   ☐ Opaque

   ☐ Porous

   ☐ Non-conductive

---

3. In the image on the right, how many pickups is the guitar equipped with? *(Tick one box)*

   ☐ 1

   ☐ 2

   ☐ 3

   ☐ 4

© | Interested Bystandr | flickr.com

---

4. Which of the following are types of pickup? *(Tick one or more boxes)*

   ☐ Humbucker

   ☐ Humdinger

   ☐ Single coil

   ☐ Multi-tap

Section 3 | Band Knowledge

Part 1 | Identification | Keys

The following five questions test your knowledge of the difference between acoustic keyboards (such as a piano) and electronic keyboards (such as a synthesiser): (Tick one box for each answer)

1. Which keyboard requires a power source? ☐ Acoustic ☐ Electronic

2. Which keyboard requires occasional tuning by a skilled tuner? ☐ Acoustic ☐ Electronic

3. Which is more likely to be bulky and heavy? ☐ Acoustic ☐ Electronic

4. Which is more likely to have a headphone socket? ☐ Acoustic ☐ Electronic

5. Which keyboard has a sustain-pedal socket? ☐ Acoustic ☐ Electronic

----

True or false:

6. All acoustic pianos have strings: ☐ True ☐ False

7. Both acoustic and electronic keyboards have black keys: ☐ True ☐ False

8. Acoustic pianos have smaller keys than most electronic keyboards: ☐ True ☐ False

9. Acoustic keyboards rely on having an AC adaptor: ☐ True ☐ False

----

10. Do the images on the right feature an acoustic or an electronic keyboard? *(Tick one box for each answer)*

    Image A: ☐ Acoustic ☐ Electronic

    Image B: ☐ Acoustic ☐ Electronic

    Image C: ☐ Acoustic ☐ Electronic

    Image D: ☐ Acoustic ☐ Electronic

Part 1 | Identification | Vocals

1. Connect each of the boxes on the left with a box on the right by drawing a line between to connect them, matching the text on the left with the closest match on the right:

Tongue	Is the tube that passes air to and from the lungs
Larynx	Allows the singer to shape and articulate sounds
Diaphragm	Main voice-producing component in the body
Trachea	A dome-shaped muscle separating chest and abdomen

True or false:

2. The diaphragm and the tongue are both muscles: ☐ True   ☐ False

3. The trachea is used to direct food and drink to the stomach: ☐ True   ☐ False

4. The lungs are located below the diaphragm: ☐ True   ☐ False

The following five question refers to the labelled image on the right:

5. Which letter points to the mouth? *(Tick one box)*

   ☐ A   ☐ B   ☐ C   ☐ D   ☐ E

6. Which letter points to the diaphragm? *(Tick one box)*

   ☐ A   ☐ B   ☐ C   ☐ D   ☐ E

7. Which letter points to the lungs? *(Tick one box)*

   ☐ A   ☐ B   ☐ C   ☐ D   ☐ E

8. Which letter points to the trachea? *(Tick one box)*

   ☐ A   ☐ B   ☐ C   ☐ D   ☐ E

9. Which letter points to the larynx? *(Tick one box)*

   ☐ A   ☐ B   ☐ C   ☐ D   ☐ E

Section 3 | Band Knowledge

Part 2 | Notation & Techniques | Drums

1. What specific technique is the drummer using to play the snare drum in the image on the right? *(Tick one box)*

   ☐ Drag ruff

   ☐ Cross stick

   ☐ Flam

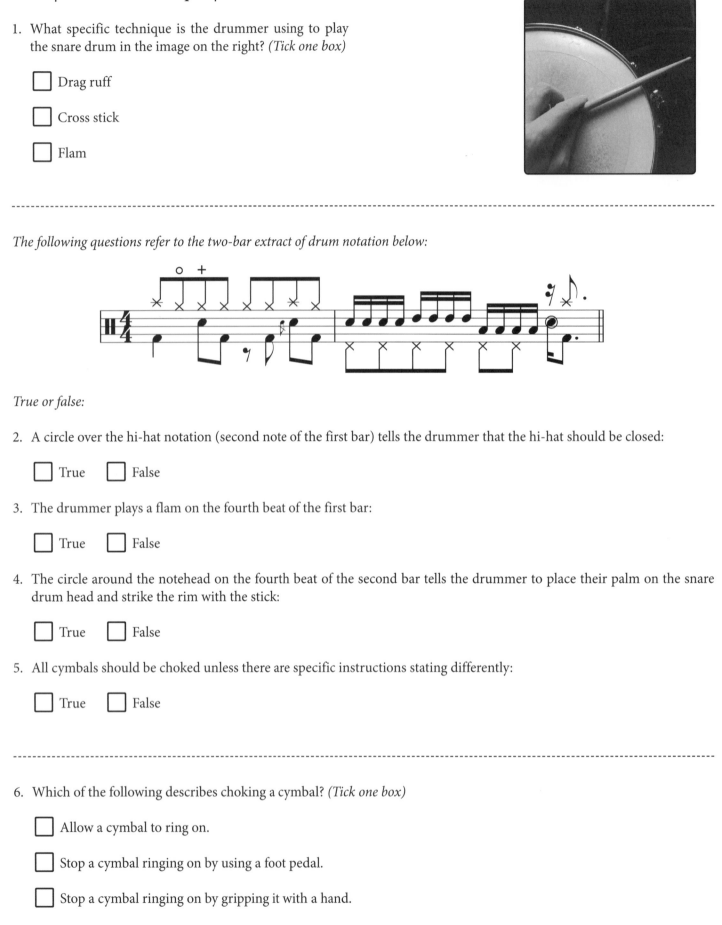

The following questions refer to the two-bar extract of drum notation below:

True or false:

2. A circle over the hi-hat notation (second note of the first bar) tells the drummer that the hi-hat should be closed:

   ☐ True   ☐ False

3. The drummer plays a flam on the fourth beat of the first bar:

   ☐ True   ☐ False

4. The circle around the notehead on the fourth beat of the second bar tells the drummer to place their palm on the snare drum head and strike the rim with the stick:

   ☐ True   ☐ False

5. All cymbals should be choked unless there are specific instructions stating differently:

   ☐ True   ☐ False

---

6. Which of the following describes choking a cymbal? *(Tick one box)*

   ☐ Allow a cymbal to ring on.

   ☐ Stop a cymbal ringing on by using a foot pedal.

   ☐ Stop a cymbal ringing on by gripping it with a hand.

Part 2 | Notation & Techniques | Guitar and Bass

The following two questions refer to the one-bar extract of guitar notation on the right:

1. How would the guitarist play the first two notes of the bar? *(Tick one box)*

   ☐ Picking both notes one quickly after the other.

   ☐ Picking the first note and bending the string up to sound the second note.

   ☐ Picking the first note then sliding up to the second note.

   ☐ Picking the first note and pulling the finger off to sound the second note.

2. The last two notes of the bar have a wavy line written above. What is this called? *(Tick one box)*

   ☐ Vibrato   ☐ Bend   ☐ Hammer-on

- -

True or false:

3. A quarter-tone bend raises the pitch upwards: ☐ True   ☐ False

4. A vibrato is achieved by detuning the string: ☐ True   ☐ False

5. PM in guitar playing means palm modulation: ☐ True   ☐ False

6. A slide is notated with a line between the two notes: ☐ True   ☐ False

- -

The following three questions relate to the two-bar extract of bass-guitar notation below:

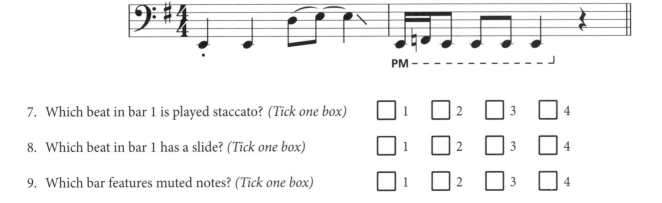

7. Which beat in bar 1 is played staccato? *(Tick one box)*   ☐ 1   ☐ 2   ☐ 3   ☐ 4

8. Which beat in bar 1 has a slide? *(Tick one box)*   ☐ 1   ☐ 2   ☐ 3   ☐ 4

9. Which bar features muted notes? *(Tick one box)*   ☐ 1   ☐ 2   ☐ 3   ☐ 4

Section 3 | Band Knowledge

Part 2 | Notation & Techniques | Keyboards

1. What do the markings below the stave mean? *(Tick one box)*

    A) They warn about the use of notes on ledger lines on
       the lower stave.
    B) They indicate when the sustain pedal should be held
       and released.
    C) They tell an organist that the lower stave should be
       played using the foot pedals.

    ☐ A   ☐ B   ☐ C

True or false:

2. Legato means to play the notes smoothly: ☐ True   ☐ False

3. Staccato means to play the notes smoothly: ☐ True   ☐ False

4. The sustain pedal dampens the sound: ☐ True   ☐ False

5. The sustain pedal is the most commonly used pedal on a piano: ☐ True   ☐ False

----

6. Where is the sustain pedal usually located on an acoustic piano? *(Tick one box)*

    A) On the left of the group of pedals.
    B) In the centre of the group of pedals.
    C) On the right of the group of pedals.

    ☐ A   ☐ B   ☐ C

True or false:

7. Pressing fully down on the sustain pedal locks it in place so that the foot can be removed from the pedal:

    ☐ True   ☐ False

8. The pedal on the left of an acoustic piano is a sustain pedal for left-footed players:

    ☐ True   ☐ False

Part 2 | Notation & Techniques | Vocals

The following questions refer to the one-bar extract of vocal music below:

1. What is the line before the first note of the bar called? *(Tick one box)*

    ☐ Fall up   ☐ Scoop up   ☐ Drop in   ☐ Lift up

2. What is the line after the final note of the bar called? *(Tick one box)*

    ☐ Scoop off   ☐ Fall off   ☐ Drop off   ☐ Lift off

True or false:

3. Lyrics always have hyphens between syllables that are part of the same word: ☐ True ☐ False

4. Lyrics only have hyphens between syllables that are a tone apart: ☐ True ☐ False

5. The word "Yesterday" should be hyphenated "Yester-day": ☐ True ☐ False

6. An *accented* note is one that is sung louder than others around it: ☐ True ☐ False

7. In the acronym *SATB*, 'T' stands for 'Throat': ☐ True ☐ False

---

The following questions refer to the one-bar extract of vocal music below:

8. Is this music written for a male or female vocalist? *(Tick one box)*

    ☐ Male   ☐ Female

9. What is the line between the fourth and fifth note called? *(Tick one box)*

    ☐ Slide   ☐ Hammer-on   ☐ Vibrato line   ☐ Portamento

BAND ANALYSIS

SUMMARY	
SECTION *(Current section highlighted)*	**MARKS**
Music Notation	20 [20%]
Popular Music Harmony	25 [25%]
Band Knowledge	25 [25%]
> **Band Analysis**	**30 [30%]**

The *Band Analysis* section of Rockschool Theory Examinations covers the following:

- 4.1 Identify general music features
- 4.2 Accurately complete a score
- 4.3 Identify instrument-specific techniques and stylistic traits
- 5.1 Identify appropriate scales for improvisation

You will be presented with a variety of exercises to hone your understanding and skills in these areas within the content specified for this grade.

Content Overview

An overview of the syllabus content covered at this grade can be found at the back of this book. As this is a cumulative syllabus, you can download overviews for all grades from the Rockschool website at *www.rockschool.co.uk*.

Section 4 | Band Analysis

Band Analysis | Example 1

The following 13 questions relate to the four-bar score below. Note that bar 3 has blank areas to be filled in as part of the tasks below:

1. What key is this piece in?

   Your answer:
   ....

2. How many B.P.M. are there in this piece?

   Your answer:
   ....

   ....

   ....

3. In bar 2, add the appropriate chord symbols over beats 1 and 3.

4. In the bar where the guitar part does *not* play any C naturals, add dynamic indications to show that all three parts should increase in volume.

5. At the start of the final bar, add an appropriate dynamic marking to show that all parts should now be playing very loudly.

6. When the drummer plays an open hi-hat, followed by a closed hi-hat, describe the technique the guitarist is using at that same point in the score:

   Your answer: ....

7. In which bar are the highest and lowest notes in the score played at the same time? *(Tick one box)*

   ☐ Bar 1   ☐ Bar 2   ☐ Bar 3   ☐ Bar 4

8. What note is played in the bass-guitar part when the guitar plays an accented chord?

   Your answer: ....

9. In which bar do all three instruments play a decrescendo? *(Tick one box)*

   ☐ Bar 1   ☐ Bar 2   ☐ Bar 3   ☐ Bar 4

10. In bars 1 & 2, there are two chords per bar, each lasting two beats. During each of these two beats, the bass plays a repeated pattern. Which of the following statements best describes this pattern? *(Tick one box)*

    ☐ The bass plays a scalic pattern based on the chords named above the score.

    ☐ The bass plays an intervallic pattern based on the key of the piece, without referencing the chords.

    ☐ The bass plays a pattern based on arpeggios of the chords named above the score.

    ☐ The bass plays a walking-bassline pattern based on the key of the piece.

11. In bars 1 to 3, add symbols to the drum part to indicate that the snare drums should be played cross stick.

(Questions continue on the next page)

Section 4 | Band Analysis

12. The style of this piece is rock. Name two musical devices used in the score which typify this style. Add the name of the instrument and a location in the score (as a bar and beat reference) where these can be found:

Musical device 1: ....

Instrument: ....

Location: ....

Musical device 2: ....

Instrument: ....

Location: ....

13. Complete the bass-guitar part by writing out a suitable cont. sim. part in bar 3.

Band Analysis | Example 2

The following 13 questions relate to the four-bar score below. Note that bar 3 has blank areas to be filled in as part of the tasks below:

1. What key is this piece in?

   Your answer: ....

(Questions continue on the next page)

Section 4 | Band Analysis

2. What information is given to you by the tempo marking in the score?

   Your answer: ....

   ....

   ....

3. Using the left hand part of the piano as a guide, add the appropriate chord symbols over the first beat of bars 1 and 2.

4. In bar 1, add the appropriate dynamic marking to show that all parts should be playing moderately loudly.

5. At the start of the final bar, add an appropriate dynamic marking to show that all parts should now be playing very loudly.

6. Which of the following statements best describes the melody played in the right-hand part of the piano? *(Tick one box)*

   ☐ The melody is scalic.

   ☐ The melody is intervallic.

   ☐ The melody is chordal.

   ☐ The melody uses arpeggios.

7. What is the pitch of the longest note in the score?

   Your answer: ....

8. What is the pitch of the highest note in the score?

   Your answer: ....

9. In which bar do all three instruments play an accent on the same beat? *(Tick one box)*

   ☐ Bar 1   ☐ Bar 2   ☐ Bar 3   ☐ Bar 4

10. Add notation to bar 3 of the score to show that the first two 16th notes played by the bass guitar should be played with a hammer-on.

11. Which musical device, often associated with funk, can be seen in the drum part?

    Your answer: ....

12. If you were to add a guitar part, what musical device could you use that would add more of a rock feel to the piece?

    Your answer: ....

    ....

13. Complete the left hand of the piano part by writing out a suitable cont. sim. part in bar 3.

Section 4 | Band Analysis

Band Analysis | Example 3

The following 13 questions relate to the four-bar score below. Note that bar 3 has blank areas to be filled in as part of the tasks below:

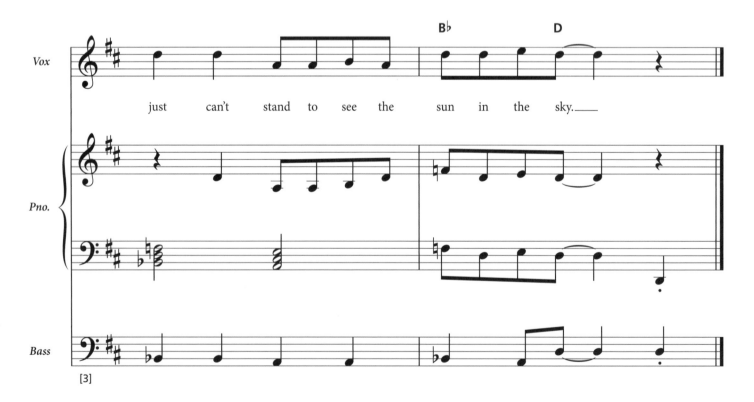

[3]

1. Name the major key, and its relative minor, that share the same key signature as the one used in this piece:

   Your answer: ....

2. Explain the meaning of the symbols located immediately to the right of the tempo marking:

   Your answer: ....

   ....

   ....

3. In bar 3, add the appropriate chord symbols over beat 1 and beat 3.

4. What is the pitch of the lowest note in the score?

   Your answer: ....

5. Add dynamic markings to show that all the instruments should play very quietly at the start of the piece.

6. Which of the following play chords at least once in the score? *(Tick one or more boxes)*

   ☐ Vocals   ☐ Piano   ☐ Bass guitar

7. In bars 1 & 2 of the piano part, what is the harmonic interval consistently used between the left- and right-hand notes?

   Your answer: ....

8. Name the scale used for the melody in the vocal part:

   Your answer: ....

9. Name the pitch of the note with an accidental in bar 4 of the bass-guitar part:

   Your answer: ....

(Questions continue on the next page)

Section 4 | Band Analysis

10. Name and define the articulation on the longest note in the piece:

   Your answer: ....

11. In which bar do the vocal line and the right hand of the piano part play the same rhythm throughout? *(Tick one box)*

   ☐ Bar 1   ☐ Bar 2   ☐ Bar 3   ☐ Bar 4

12. Name two musical devices used in the score which are typical of blues. Add the name of the instrument and a location in the score (as a bar and beat reference) where these can be found:

   Musical device 1: ....

   Instrument: ....

   Location: ....

   Musical device 2: ....

   Instrument: ....

   Location: ....

13. Complete bar 2 of the bass-guitar part by writing out a suitable cont. sim. part.

SAMPLE PAPER

The following pages contain examples of the types of questions you will find in a Grade 3 exam paper. They give an indication of the content, format, layout and level at this grade.

You will see the exam paper has been split into the same four sections that have been presented earlier in this workbook:

- Music Notation
- Popular Music Harmony
- Band Knowledge
- Band Analysis

Content Overview

- **Marking:**
  - The exam is marked out of a total of 100, and the total available marks for each section are clearly stated at the start of each section. There is also a blank markbox where your total examination score can be noted.
  - The total marks available for each question are displayed on the right, and include a space for your teacher to mark your answers.

- **General advice:**
  - If a question requires a written answer, don't feel compelled to use every line. Answering the question correctly is much more important than using all the available space.
  - Aim to answer all the questions set. If you get stuck on one particular question, move on and come back to it later.

- **Neatness:**
  - Your answers should be neat, accurate and legible as marks cannot be given if your response is ambiguous.
  - Avoid unnecessary corrections by thinking your responses through before committing them to paper.
  - Use a pencil that is sharp enough to write precisely, but soft enough to rub out and make corrections.
  - To avoid confusion, tick boxes (checkboxes) should be marked with a clear tick symbol rather than a cross. Please note that some answers require more than one box to be ticked, so read the questions carefully.

Please visit *www.rockschool.co.uk* for detailed information on all Rockschool examinations, including syllabus guides, marking schemes and examination entry information.

Section 1 | Music Notation

Total marks for this section: 20

Mark:

Q 1.01 | Identify the missing time signature: *(Tick one box)*

1

☐ 2/4   ☐ 3/4   ☐ 4/4   ☐ 6/8   ☐ 12/8

Q 1.02 | Identify the missing time signature: *(Tick one box)*

1

☐ 2/4   ☐ 3/4   ☐ 4/4   ☐ 6/8   ☐ 12/8

Q 1.03 | Identify the missing note as indicated with a question mark: *(Tick one box)*

1

☐ ♪.   ☐ ♪   ☐ ♪   ☐ ♩

Q 1.04 | Identify the missing note as indicated with a question mark: *(Tick one box)*

1

☐ ♩.   ☐ ♪.   ☐ ♪   ☐ 𝅗𝅥

Q 1.05 | Identify the missing rest as indicated with a question mark: *(Tick one box)* [1]

☐ 𝄾   ☐ 𝄾.   ☐ 𝄿   ☐ 𝄼.

Q 1.06 | Identify the missing rest as indicated with a question mark: *(Tick one box)* [1]

☐ 𝄼.   ☐ 𝄾.   ☐ 𝄾   ☐ 𝄿

The following two questions refer to the music extract below:

Q 1.07 | Identify the correct scale name: *(Tick one box)* [1]

☐ D major   ☐ B natural minor   ☐ G major

☐ E natural minor   ☐ A natural minor

Q 1.08 | Identify the missing clef: [1]

Your answer: ....

Grade 3 | Sample Paper

The following two questions refer to the music extract below:

Q 1.09 | Identify the correct scale name: *(Tick one box)* [1]

☐ E♭ major   ☐ E natural minor   ☐ A major

☐ C natural minor   ☐ A natural minor

Q 1.10 | Identify the missing clef: [1]

Your answer: ....

Q 1.11 | Write down the sequence of letters that represents the order in which the following bars are played from the start to the finish. [3]

Your answer: ....

Q 1.12 | Add a rest of the correct length above each question mark so that each bar fits the time signature: [2]

Q 1.13 | *The following five questions relate to the music extract below:* 〔5〕

Which bar contains a crescendo?

Your answer: ....

Which bar contains a dynamic marking telling the player to play very quietly?

Your answer: ....

Which bar does not contain an accented note?

Your answer: ....

In the right hand, which articulation is used on the first note of the fifth bar?

Your answer: ....

Which bar contains a diminuendo?

Your answer: ....

Section 2 | Popular Music Harmony

Q 2.01 | Identify the following two melodic intervals and write your answers on the lines below each example: `2`

....

Q 2.02 | Add a note above each of the notes to create the requested harmonic interval: `3`

minor 3rd   perfect 5th   octave

Q 2.03 | Using whole notes, write a one-octave *descending* scale of D minor pentatonic. Add the correct key signature if needed: `5`

Q 2.04 | Using whole notes, write a one-octave *descending* scale of A major pentatonic. Add the correct key signature if needed: `5`

Q 2.05 | Using whole notes, complete the stave below by adding the notes of an *ascending* and *descending* one-octave arpeggio in the **major** key shown by the clef and key signature: `5`

Q 2.06 | Identify the following chords using Roman numerals. The first chord has been identified for you:

[3]

I _____   _____   _____   _____

Q 2.07 | Using whole notes, add the notes of the triads given in Roman numerals. The first chord has been completed for you:

[2]

I   II m   III m

Section 3 | Band Knowledge | Part 1 – Identification

Total marks for this section: [25]

Mark: [   ]

Q 3.01 | Which tool is used to adjust the tension on a drum to raise or lower the pitch?

[1]

Your answer: ....

Q 3.02 | Which type of drum is usually mounted in pairs?

[1]

Your answer: ....

Q 3.03 | Which common cymbal is used for occasional accents?

[1]

Your answer: ....

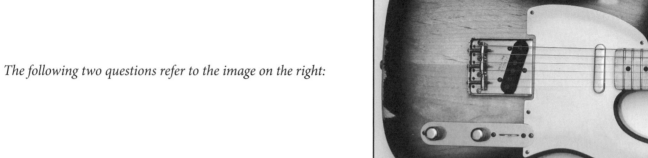

The following two questions refer to the image on the right:

Q 3.04 | What type of guitar is shown in the image?

Your answer: ....

Q 3.05 | In the image, how many pickups is the guitar equipped with?

Your answer: ....

Q 3.06 | Name a type of common pickup:

Your answer: ....

Q 3.07 | What is the name of the numerous thin metal strips inserted into the fingerboard of the guitar and bass guitar?

Your answer: ....

Q 3.08 | Give three different ways in which an acoustic piano is physically different from an electronic keyboard:

A: ....

B: ....

C: ....

The following three questions refer to the labelled image on the right:

Q 3.09 | Name the body-part labelled 'A':

1

Your answer: ....

Q 3.10 | Name the body-part labelled 'B':

1

Your answer: ....

Q 3.11 | Name the body-part labelled 'C':

1

Your answer: ....

Grade 3 | Sample Paper

Section 3 | Band Knowledge | Part 2 – Notation & Techniques

The following three questions relate to the two-bar extract of drum notation below:

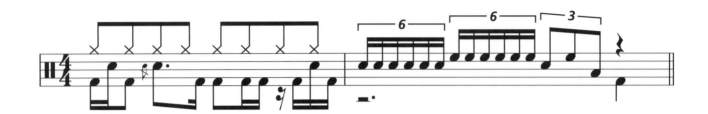

Q 3.12 | What symbol would need to be added above the first note of the extract in order to indicate that the hi-hat should be played open? `1`

Your answer: ....

Q 3.13 | On which beat of the first bar is there a flam? `1`

Your answer: ....

Q 3.14 | Which tom is not played in this extract? `1`

Your answer: ....

The following three questions relate to the one-bar extract of guitar notation on the right:

Q 3.15 | On the first beat of the bar, what does the upward curved arrow with a ¼ sign mean? `1`

Your answer: ....

Q 3.16 | What does the wavy line over the final two tied notes mean? *(Tick one box)* `1`

☐ Slide ☐ Vibrato ☐ Pull-off ☐ Hammer-on

Q 3.17 | How would the first two notes of beat 3 be played (i.e. the grace note and 16th triplet note)? `1`

Your answer: ....

- -

The following three tasks require you to add notation to the one-bar extract of piano music on the right:

Q 3.18 | Draw the correct symbols on the extract to show that the pedal should be pressed down on the first beat of the bar and released after the final note of the bar. `1`

Q 3.19 | In the right-hand part, draw the correct symbol to show that the last four notes of the extract should be played legato. `1`

Q 3.20 | In the left-hand part, add a tenuto mark to the first note of the bar. `1`

Grade 3 | Sample Paper

The following three questions relate to the one-bar extract of vocal notation on the right:

You   ask   for hearts and flow - ers

Q 3.21 | What is the line before the first note of the bar called?

1

Your answer: ....

Q 3.22 | How should the lyric "flow-ers'" be sung?

1

Your answer: ....

Q 3.23 | How can you tell that this extract would be sung by a male voice?

1

Your answer: ....

Section 4 | Band Analysis

The following 13 questions relate to the four-bar score below. Note that bar 3 has blank areas that are to be filled in as part of the tasks that follow:

Grade 3 | Sample Paper

Q 4.01 | Name the key used in this piece: `1`

Your answer: ....

Q 4.02 | Is this piece swung, and how can you tell? `1`

Your answer: ....

....

Q 4.03 | Write the correct chord names over beat 1 of bars 1 & 2. `2`

Q 4.04 | One of the bars contains a prominent fill. Name the instrument and bar in which this happens: `2`

Your answer: ....

Q 4.05 | Add accents to bar 3 of the bass guitar where the bass is playing the root note of the chord. `3`

Q 4.06 | How many times is the lowest-pitched note in the score played? `1`

Your answer: ....

Q 4.07 | Which bar or bars do *not* contain a crash cymbal? *(Tick one or more boxes)* `1`

☐ Bar 1   ☐ Bar 2   ☐ Bar 3   ☐ Bar 4

Q 4.08 | Add three dynamic markings to bar 1 to show that the music should increase from moderately loud on beat 1 to very loud on beat 4. `3`

Q 4.09 | How are the first two hi-hats in bar 3 played? *(Tick one box)* `1`

☐ Open then closed   ☐ Closed then open   ☐ Both open   ☐ Both closed

Q 4.10 | In bar 1 of the left hand of the piano part, add an articulation on an off-beat note to show that the note should be played short and detached. `1`

Q 4.11 | In bar 3 of the left hand of the piano part, add the missing rests where indicated by an asterisk. `2`

Q 4.12 | The style of this piece is pop. Name two musical devices used in the score which typify this style. Add the name of the instrument and a location in the score (as a bar and beat reference) where these can be found:

6

Musical device 1: ....

Instrument: ....

Location: ....

Musical device 2: ....

Instrument: ....

Location: ....

Q 4.13 | Complete the right hand of the piano part by writing out a suitable cont. sim. part in bar 3.

6

Syllabus Content Overview | Grade 3

Important: This table represents content that is new at this grade. The content of Rockschool Theory Examinations is cumulative, so Grades 1 to 8 include all content from previous grades in the syllabus. A full version of this table is available online at *www.rockschool.co.uk*, and includes details of content at every grade.

Section	Content	Details
1: Music Notation (20%)	1.1: Pitch	note range: bass clef (A1–G4), treble clef (F3–E5)
		enharmonic pitch names
	1.2: Note length/rhythm	note lengths: quarter note triplet, eighth-note triplet
		time signatures: $\frac{3}{8}$ $\frac{6}{8}$ $\frac{12}{8}$
	1.3: Dynamics, articulations, phrasing	D.S., D.C., al Coda
		dynamics: pianissimo, fortissimo
		articulations: vibrato, fermata
		tempo: swing notation
2: Popular Music Harmony (25%)	2.1: Scales and related intervals	major scales: A, E♭
		natural minor scales: F♯m, Cm
		harmonised major scale: diatonic chords
		major and minor pentatonic scale formula
		major pentatonic scale: C, G, D, A, F, B♭, E♭
		minor pentatonic scales: Am, Em, Bm, F♯m, Dm, Gm, Cm
		harmonic and melodic intervals: perfect 4th, perfect 5th
	2.2: Simple triadic chords	major chords: A, E♭
		major arpeggios: A, E♭
		minor chords: F♯m, Cm
		minor arpeggios: F♯m, Cm
		harmonised major scale: diatonic chords
		Roman numerals and chord charts
3: Band Knowledge (25%)	3.1: Identify instrument parts and function	drums: tuning key, cymbal stand
		guitar and bass guitar: tuning pegs, pickups
		keys: basic differences between an acoustic and electric keyboard
		vocals: larynx, diaphragm
	3.2: Identify instrument-specific notation	drum notation: cross stick, choked cymbals
		guitar and bass guitar notation: string bends, vibrato, quarter-tone bend
		keys notation: pedal notation
		vocal notation: fall off, scoop in
	3.3: Identify instrumental techniques	as listed above in 3.2
4: Band Analysis (30%)	4.1: Identify general music features listed within criteria 1, 2 and 3 within a score	identify and show understanding of the applied musical elements listed within the first three sections (above) within the context of a score
		instrument range: drums (hi-hat, snare drum, bass drum, crash cymbal, ride cymbal, toms), guitar, bass guitar, keyboard, vocals
		number of parts: 3
		piece length: 4 bars
	4.2: Accurately complete a score	1 bar cont. sim. part for any of the instruments listed within the 3 part score
	4.3: Identify instrument-specific techniques and stylistic traits	as listed within part 3 (above)
		identify musical and stylistic devices used within the score (pop, blues, rock, metal, funk)
	5.1: Identify appropriate scales for improvisation	be able to identify appropriate scale for improvising a solo over a chord sequence within the score

rockschool®

ENTER ONLINE

Ready to take your Rockschool Theory Exam?

Now it's easier than ever...

1 GO TO WWW.ROCKSCHOOL.CO.UK/ENTER-ONLINE

2 CREATE AN ACCOUNT

3 SELECT YOUR EXAM CENTRE AND DATE

4 CHOOSE YOUR GRADE

...and you're ready to go.

Book your exam today – go to **www.rockschool.co.uk/enter-online**, or email **info@rockschool.co.uk** for more information.